This book belongs to

....

This is a Parragon Publishing Book
This edition published in 2006

Parragon Publishing
Queen Street House
4 Queen Street
Bath BA1 1HE, UK

Created by small world creations ltd
Printed in China
ISBN 1-40545-359-1

A B C

A First Letters Book

p

a

a is for apples, that are sweet and juicy!

b

b is for ball, and balloons *that float!*

C

c is for coat, which keeps me warm.

d

d is for duck that floats in my bathtub.

e

e is for

eggs with

dippy yolks.

f

f is for fingers -
I've got ten!

g

h

g is for the girl next door
h is for the house she lives in.

i

i is for
ice at the
skating
rink.

j

j is for **jar**
of sticky strawberry **jelly.**

k

l

k is for **kitten** who likes to purr,
l is for **lion** who likes to roar!

m

m is for
mommy
who cuddles
me every
night!

n

n is for **nose.** My teddy bear's nose is big and soft.

o is for **owl**
that hoots at night!

p

p is for presents
that I get on my birthday!

q

q is for
queen
who wears a gold crown.

r

s

r is for **rainbow**,

s is for

sun in the

sky.

✝ t is for train that chugs through the tunnel.

u

u is for **umbrella**
with the yellow spots!

V

W

v is for **violins** that can screech,
w is for **whistles** that peep!

X

x is
for the
x-ray
I had
at the
hospital.

y

y is for **yellow**, which
is our favorite color!

Z

z is for the sound we make when we're tucked up in bed.